Gulliver's Travels

A graphic classic by
ADAM **G**RANT

Based on the novel by
JONATHAN **S**WIFT

SCHOLASTIC INC.
New York Toronto London Auckland Sydney
Mexico City New Delhi Hong Kong

Penciller
George O'Connor

Layouts
Greg Follender

Colors, Inks, and Letters
Digital Chameleon

Cover Art
Michael Lilly

Project Management
Michael Apice

1 2 3 4 5 6 7 8 9 10   23   08 07 06 05 04 03 02 01

Gulliver's Travels

Jonathan Swift's life was as exciting as his books. He was born in Ireland in 1667. When he was still a baby, his nurse kidnapped him and took him to England. He was returned to his mother at age three. By then he could already spell and read.

When he grew up, Swift wrote books that point out the silly things that humans do. His most famous book is Gulliver's Travels. It makes fun of the English government and its laws.

In this book, an ordinary man named Gulliver has some very strange adventures. The first one takes place in the made-up land of Lilliput. Lilliput is a lot like England in the 1700s -- only much, much smaller!

IT WAS THE YEAR 1699. THE NAME OF THE SHIP WAS THE ANTELOPE. I, LEMUEL GULLIVER, WAS THE SHIP'S DOCTOR. ON MAY 4TH, WE LEFT ENGLAND. WE WERE HEADED FOR THE EAST INDIES.

AFTER SEVERAL MONTHS AT SEA, WE HIT SOME VERY BAD WEATHER. IN THE MIDDLE OF THE STORM, OUR SHIP HIT A ROCK AND SPLIT IN TWO.

I WAS KNOCKED FROM THE SHIP. FOR TWO LONG DAYS I MANAGED TO SURVIVE BY SWIMMING.

FINALLY, I FELT LAND UNDER MY FEET. I STRUGGLED ONTO THE SHORE AND FELL INTO A DEEP SLEEP.

Land! At last!

THEY BUILT A PLATFORM SO THAT A GOVERNMENT OFFICIAL COULD SPEAK TO ME FACE TO FACE.

Now then, Man Mountain. Do you need anything to make you more comfortable?

Well... I am very hungry and thirsty.

This monster will eat all the food in the kingdom!

Right! He'll eat us all out of house and home.

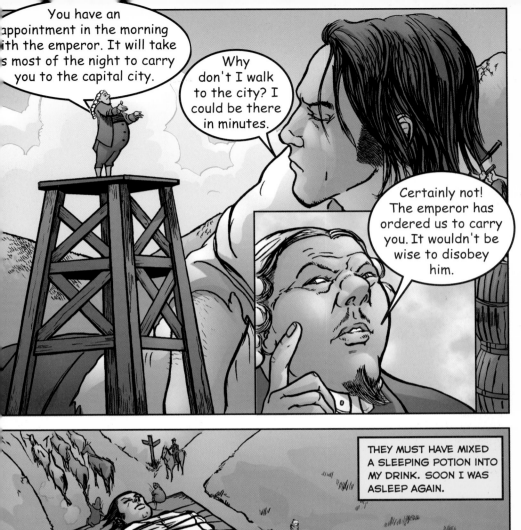

You have an appointment in the morning with the emperor. It will take us most of the night to carry you to the capital city.

Why don't I walk to the city? I could be there in minutes.

Certainly not! The emperor has ordered us to carry you. It wouldn't be wise to disobey him.

THEY MUST HAVE MIXED A SLEEPING POTION INTO MY DRINK. SOON I WAS ASLEEP AGAIN.

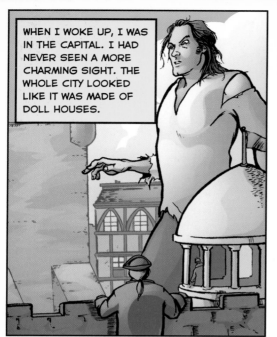

WHEN I WOKE UP, I WAS IN THE CAPITAL. I HAD NEVER SEEN A MORE CHARMING SIGHT. THE WHOLE CITY LOOKED LIKE IT WAS MADE OF DOLL HOUSES.

AN ABANDONED CASTLE WAS TO BE MY HOME. BUT I WAS STILL A PRISONER. I WAS CHAINED TO MY HOME AT THE LEG.

I must find a way to gain my freedom...

AT LAST, THE EMPEROR CAME TO SEE ME WITH LORD BOLGOLAM, THE ADMIRAL OF THE NAVY. I WAS TOLD TO LIE DOWN. NO ONE WAS ALLOWED TO BE TALLER THAN HIS MAJESTY.

Quite right.

Not too close, Majesty! We don't know anything about this man.

Welcome to Lilliput, Man Mountain. What brought you to these parts?

I don't know, your Majesty. I'm not even sure where these parts are.

Lord Bolgolam here told me you were a giant. But I never dreamed you were this big.

In my country, your Majesty, I'm not even considered tall.

Is there anything you would like, Man Mountain?

I would very much like my freedom, your Majesty.

What do you think, Lord Bolgolam? Can we trust the giant?

I would advise against it, your Majesty. We don't know anything about him. He could be very dangerous.

I'll discuss your request with my advisors, Man Mountain. In the meantime, we shall keep you well fed and comfortable.

BUT I HAD TROUBLE GETTING COMFORTABLE IN LILLIPUT. THE EMPEROR SEEMED NICE ENOUGH. BUT SOME OF THE TOWNSPEOPLE DIDN'T LIKE ME. THEY YELLED UP AT ME AND SHOT ARROWS. ONE ARROW JUST MISSED MY LEFT EYE.

Why don't these people just leave me alone?

FINALLY I HAD HAD ENOUGH. SO, I DECIDED TO PLAY A TRICK ON MY TORMENTORS.

Help

AFTERWARDS, I WAS TREATED MUCH BETTER BY THE LILLIPUTIANS. I EVEN MADE A NEW FRIEND. HIS NAME WAS RELDRESAL.

A FEW WEEKS LATER, THE EMPEROR CAME TO SEE ME WITH GREAT NEWS.

You are hereby granted your freedom. But there are a few conditions. One, you can't leave Lilliput without permission. Two, you can't step on our citizens...

Your Majesty, I agree to everything.

ONE CONDITION OF MY FREEDOM WAS TO HELP WITH BIG CONSTRUCTION PROJECTS.

Thanks for your help, Man Mountain!

Now, repeat after me...

I ALSO HAD TO SWEAR MY LOYALTY TO LILLIPUT. AND I HAD TO FIGHT FOR LILLIPUT IN THE WAR.

HEAR YE HEAR YE

His father, the emperor, made a new law. From that day on, all Lilliputians must cut off only the small end of their eggs. Even now, people who cut off the large end of their egg may be punished by death!

But some people didn't want to be told which end of their egg to cut off. They escaped to Blefuscu, our rival kingdom...

...and pledged their loyalty to the Blefuscan king.

EARLY ONE MORNING, THE EMPEROR SENT A MESSENGER TO MY DOOR. I WAS SUPPOSED TO COME TO THE WAR ROOM OF THE ROYAL PALACE RIGHT AWAY.

TERRIBLE NEWS HAD REACHED THE PALACE. THE BLEFUSCANS WERE PREPARING TO ATTACK. THE EMPEROR AND HIS MINISTERS WERE TRYING TO DECIDE WHAT TO DO.

Loyal ministers, I've asked our Man Mountain to join us. His great size and strength may help us against our enemies.

FOR SOME REASON, ADMIRAL BOLGOLAM DID NOT LOOK HAPPY TO SEE ME IN THE WAR ROOM.

As you know, the Blefuscans have a large navy. My spies have been watching them. They say that the Blefuscans are getting their warships ready to attack our beloved kingdom!

We must prepare our troops for a long, bloody war.

I WAITED UNTIL SUNSET. THEN I HEADED OUT FOR BLEFUSCU. I HAD A PLAN.

IT TOOK ME A FEW HOURS TO ROUND UP ALL OF BLEFUSCU'S WARSHIPS. I HOOKED THEM ALL TOGETHER. THEN I STARTED TOWING THE SHIPS BACK TO LILLIPUT.

SOMEONE MUST HAVE SOUNDED AN ALARM. SOON AN ANGRY ARMY OF BLEFUSCANS WAS STANDING ON THE SHORE, FIRING AT ME.

I RETURNED TO A HERO'S WELCOME IN LILLIPUT.

Thank you, your Highness. I am deeply touched.

THE EMPORER GAVE ME THE TITLE OF NARDAC, THE HIGHEST HONOR IN THE LAND.

I'm not even a Nardac.

THAT NIGHT I HAD A SECRET VISITOR. A BLEFUSCAN OFFICIAL HAD COME TO LILLIPUT TO SEE ME.

My king hears that you refused to invade Blefuscu.

He is grateful to you for saving his people. You are welcome anytime in Blefuscu as a guest of the king.

Thank you. Please tell your king that he is most kind.

I KNEW THE EMPEROR'S MEN WOULD COME AFTER ME. SO I WASTED NO TIME. I LEFT FOR BLEFUSCU.

Welcome to Blefuscu. And yet, I seem to remember that you've been here once before.

SUDDENLY, I WAS SCARED. I HAD STOLEN THEIR ENTIRE NAVY. PERHAPS THEY WANTED TO BLIND ME, TOO.

But this time, I'm afraid we're all out of ships.

Although you stole our navy, you saved our country from slavery. You are a hero here. How can we help you?

With all due respect, your Majesty, I would like to go home.

AS LUCK WOULD HAVE IT, I FOUND A ROWBOAT IN THE SEA NOT FAR FROM BLEFUSCU.

IT WAS A CRISP, SUNNY MORNING. AND I HEADED OUT ON THE VAST, BLUE OCEAN, HOPING TO MAKE MY WAY HOME.

Best of luck to you, Gulliver!

AFTER ONLY A WEEK, I CAME UPON A GRAND ENGLISH SHIP. THE CAPTAIN INVITED ME ABOARD, AND I SAILED FOR HOME, MY STRANGE ORDEAL AT AN END. WHAT HAPPENED NEXT IS ANOTHER STORY....

How good it will be to return home!

The End